BOLD'S FOLD

BY DARREN

TONY BOLD MINISTRIES INC.

EASTBOURNE

Published by
KINGSWAY PUBLICATIONS
Lottbridge Drove, Eastbourne, BN23 6NT, England.
Email: books@kingsway.co.uk

Designed and produced for the publishers by
Bookprint Creative Services, P.O. Box 827, BN21 3YJ, England.
Printed in Great Britain.

Foreword

We're involved in a very serious business as Christians. Following God, resisting temptation and loving our neighbours could change the world.

But it's not without its lighter moments, as the writer of Proverbs seemed to grasp. He reminds us that a 'cheerful heart is good medicine'. Holy mirth can sometimes inject some reality when things become a little intense – keeping our gentle scepticism about the eccentric, the fanatical or the downright weird, from turning into cynicism.

So, if you discover your favourite aspect of church life in these pages coming under the humour microscope, please don't assume it's a crusade against it. Prayer, worship, healing, counselling, deliverance and prophecy are all a valuable part of church life. But, in the midst of the serious business, it is just so funny sometimes.

by Dave Roberts

happier all the time!

By way of an introduction . . .

Tony Bold is husband to Janet Bold, father to Cliff and Bunty Bold, and pastor of a church of unspecified denominational background, nicknamed by its members as 'Bold's Fold' (although known locally to non-members as 'the Nut Ranch'). The following excerpts from the Pastor's personal diary are used with permission . . .

TUESDAY 20 MARCH

I've got a headache. It's the leaders meetings that do it to me. After I let Janet bring along her knitting I couldn't really refuse any of the others getting on with their hobbies too. I'm concerned they're gradually escalating unnoticed, however. Discussing our recent communication problems over the noise of Brenton's lathe soon wears you down.

SUNDAY 25 MARCH

The children had a separate service in the back room this morning. Their worship was really taking off. It is lovely to hear children worshipping their heavenly Father — laughing, dancing, playing their little instruments, etc. But just not when I'm trying to preach, so I nipped round the back and turned their power off.

NEIL HADN'T QUITE GOT THE HANG OF 'GETTING A PICTURE'

SUNDAY 1 APRIL

What a morning! Although I had no time to prepare my sermon, I somehow managed to deliver what in retrospect I can see as being the most powerful, hard-hitting yet beautifully poignant message of my career. Before I'd even arrived at the penultimate hamster metaphor, people (complete strangers even) began coming forward to be saved! I've never seen anything like it! What an incredible time it was for us all. There was weeping on earth and rejoicing in heaven. Hallelujah!

MONDAY 2 APRIL

It seems there was no rejoicing in heaven after all ... just a lot of idiots laughing down here. And at my expense. Typical of me to forget yesterday's date, and downright typical of my 'hilarious' congregation to remember it.

NO ONE PARTICULARLY LIKED ROGER

SUNDAY 8 APRIL

There was an Indian in our service today. Not a West Indian mind you — a full-blooded Red Indian! Complete with feather headdress, beads, face paint and a war axe. He sat right in front all through my talk and then he left. I managed to catch up with him outside and he said he'd been expecting a different meeting and must have gotten his times muddled up. I'm going to have to enquire what else this hall is used for I think.

FORTUNATELY DUNCAN WAS WEARING HIS MINISTRY TEAM L-PLATE
AND ALLOWANCES COULD BE MADE

TUESDAY 17 APRIL

Wouldn't you know it! The first time I wear my tank top in church and I get a great long letter from Roger detailing his deep concern over the 'subtle infiltration of Satan's armour of darkness into our midst'. I was reportedly flaunting my 'tank top of temptation' with wanton disregard as to the consequences that my demonic apparel would wreak on our unenlightened congregation. In addition to all of this, I have been supplied with a detailed diagram clearly outlining the full inventory of the enemy's armour which includes: the flares of adultery; the loafers of discontent; and the mittens of perversity. I think Roger needs a job.

TIGHT SECURITY AT THE WORSHIP CONFERENCE

FRIDAY 20 APRIL

Had a dream last night that aliens invaded our church and started vaporizing random members of the congregation. I don't know how it ended because Janet kicked me and said all my laughing was keeping her awake.

PAM SENSED SHE WAS UNDER ATTACK

SUNDAY 29 APRIL

Our new songbooks arrived today. Naturally all the religious old duffers kicked up a right fuss. You'd think they'd be happy we were moving with the times, incorporating modern imagery, maintaining relevance to the youth, etc. But oh no. Apparently words like 'foxy', 'homeboys' and 'B. K. Flamer' have no place in corporate worship. As for songs such as 'Your love is my mothership' and 'Rather you than smack' — well, you'd think we were raving heretics, they made such a carry on. What a stuffy old bunch.

SATURDAY 5 MAY

Cliff went out to a college party last night. I told him to make sure he's back by 10.30 at the latest. He arrived home at 10.25. I wasn't expecting him till at least 1.00! He worries me sometimes.

3 HOURS INTO THE PRAYER MEETING ROB'S DECEPTION IS UNCOVERED

WEDNESDAY 9 MAY

I do love talking to little children. They say the most adorable things. When I arrived at Tel and Stella's home group tonight, little Mindy wanted me to lift her onto the window ledge so she could look for pigs! When I asked her why she was looking for pigs she said she'd overheard mummy telling daddy that they could keep the new tv and video so long as pigs didn't catch him! Such active imaginations children have! Tel whisked her off to bed then, but I did promise to listen out for any oinking!

UNFORTUNATELY NO ONE NOTICED IAN 'GO DOWN IN THE SPIRIT' BEHIND THE PIANO AT THE EVENING'S RENEWAL MEETING

SUNDAY 13 MAY

Singen brought along his latest invention for a road test this morning. It was called a DTA (Dodgy Theology Alarm) and contained the entire Bible encoded and cross-referenced in its memory. Once set by the main speaker, it basically monitors every word spoken. Anything doctrinally unsound triggers the warning siren. I had high hopes for it to put an end to some of the crackpot testimonies and notices we get here, but unfortunately there seemed to be a basic design flaw — the stupid thing was going off every two minutes all through my sermon.

WEDNESDAY 16 MAY

I've decided to make up a diagram of our 'church body', assigning every member a body part that I see them symbolically mirroring within their particular ministry. I think it should help us all see where we fit and appreciate the roles each other plays...

FRIDAY 18 MAY

Have run into difficulties matching people to their relevant body parts. What ministry shares any symbolic similarities with the moustache for example? I considered something perhaps unfashionable such as evangelism, except I had that down as being long toe nails (something that isn't particularly pleasant, but needs attending to none the less). It is possible I've made my body diagram too detailed.

SUNDAY 20 MAY

Displayed my finished church body diagram this morning. It went down extremely well with everyone except Roger, who typically made a right song and dance over his assigned body part. I tried to point out to him that while that particular anatomical feature may not be seen as necessarily desirable, it is still an essential component in any fully functional human body. That did little to placate him, however, and he has reportedly left the church. The diagram was a roaring success on all accounts then.

IN PREPARATION FOR HIS INTERNATIONAL SIGNS AND WONDERS MINISTRY LIONEL WOULD PRAY FOR THE RESURRECTION OF ROADKILL

MONDAY 21 MAY

Roger telephoned tonight to inform me that he wouldn't be leaving after all, but felt there were issues between us. He believes that I have failed to come alongside him in his ministry and have allowed my reservations over his calling to cloud my judgement of his character, leading him to conclude I do not value, respect and, above all, love him as a fellow believer and brother in Christ. What a jerk.

THE FAMILY SERVICE: A RELAXED AND ACCESSIBLE ENVIRONMENT
ONE CAN SAFELY USE TO INTRODUCE PEOPLE TO THE CHURCH

FRIDAY 25 MAY

My book on effective evangelism is surprisingly inspiring. I finished the chapter headed 'Sensitivity in Sharing' just before I went to the dentist today. Drawing on what I'd been reading concerning the pressures of modern life leaving us so few opportunities for receptivity to the gospel, I was able to recognize just how stressed the dentist was and focus the main thrust of my witnessing on the ability of God's transcendent peace to release her from the crushing burdens of the world. I'm not sure it went down all that well actually. She gave me one heck of an injection — my mouth's still numb. I might read that chapter again.

SUNDAY 3 JUNE

Cliff said the sermon this morning provided a doctrinal breakthrough in his theological understanding and will surely inspire him to new levels in his personal devotions. I suggested to Janet that we take him for counselling.

SUNDAY 10 JUNE

Alan asked if he could run the children's games again at our forthcoming summer picnic. I did point out that while last year's re-enactment of Elijah and the prophets of Baal was very creative, it did result in at least half the children being treated for minor burns, as well as near prosecution from the Forestry Commission. He said he was thinking about the destruction of Sodom and Gomorrah this year. I suggested it might be nice to let somebody else have a turn.

SUNDAY 17 JUNE

Ivan stood up this morning and brazenly informed us that next Sunday evening he and his little group would be conducting a twilight meeting aiming to rediscover the joys and wonders of animal sacrifice! Quite how he thinks he can get away with an announcement like that is beyond me. I told him straight that I will be calling on him at 8.00 sharp tomorrow night to discuss this so-called meeting.

MONDAY 18 JUNE

Sorted it all out with Ivan. It was all a big misunderstanding in the end. He'd completely forgotten about our open party next Sunday, and agreed to move his animal killing thing to the weekend after.

IT NEVER OCCURRED TO BRENTON THAT
HIS BREATH MIGHT BE THE CAUSE OF HIS 'POWERFUL ANOINTING' THAT MORNING

SUNDAY 24 JUNE

I had a number of requests after last Sunday's ministry time to pastorally advise Brenton on the benefits of dental hygiene. I thought taking him aside might prove too authoritarian and decided the most sensible course of action would be to make a little joke out of it when we next spoke. Unfortunately it didn't go down too well, and he was terribly offended. Janet maintains I should've stopped my impression short of vomiting, but I think some people are just too highly strung.

SUNDAY 1 JULY

Had an absolute deluge of complaints following this afternoon's picnic. Lionel's organized games for the children apparently consisted of his rowing them out into the middle of the river followed by a race — the first to walk to the riverbank wins. Naturally nobody won since they all sank, whereby Lionel rebuked them severely for their lack of faith. I gave Lionel a call and politely suggested his expectations of the children were unreasonable and even dangerous. In my understanding of Scripture, Peter walked on the Sea of Tiberias — salt water, not fresh water. I suggested he should hire a fishing boat and try it again a few miles off shore if he wants to do it properly.

SUNDAY 8 JULY

Ian spoke this morning on the 'pull of the world' and how modern culture is demonically manipulated to undermine and destroy Christian values. All very interesting, but a touch theatrical I feel. Anybody who's been involved with charismatic Christianity for as long as I have, knows full well that the primary focus for demonic activity is to confuse the Lord's elect and ultimately make them late for church on Sunday mornings.

DUDLEY WAS EX-ANGLICAN. APPARENTLY ONLY DAVE HAD REMEMBERED

SUNDAY 15 JULY

We half drowned little Wayne trying to get him under the water at this afternoon's baptisms. It was his mother's fault since she insisted on him wearing a full life jacket and floats. After a pretty determined effort we finally got most of him submerged — everything except his forehead. Still — close enough! However, since they sang 'I am a new creation' on the way out, I felt it was only right to point out that although he had now been baptized into Christ's resurrection life, his forehead was still of the old flesh and consequently a slave to sin prone to temptation and death. He started crying then so I thought it best to save it for another time (and Janet says I'm not sensitive!).

SUNDAY 22 JULY

Brenton delivered a highly charged announcement today. Somebody has been fly-posting for a local night club on the wall outside, and he proposed we don the full armour of God and take a stand against this encroaching symbol of secularism. I suggested he fronted a prayer march there and then, whereby he gallantly led an enthusiastic bunch off towards the street in fervent prayer. Once they were out of the building I was able to lock the doors and get on with the service.

THURSDAY 26 JULY

Had a planning meeting tonight for my proposed 'March for Jesus' in October. Raymond pointed out that the marches are usually too long and perhaps we might aim to walk faster this year. Steven said the faster the better in his opinion, and suggested we look at a 'Run for Jesus'. Geoff was all in favour of a 'Drive for Jesus' although I was concerned the church's visibility was becoming compromised. Rob said it was precisely the level of visibility on these occasions that worried him and might we consider a 'Balloon for Jesus'. I'm sensing some opposition.

THIS WAS THE MOMENT ALAN HAD GROWN
HIS BEARD FOR

SUNDAY 5 AUGUST

The sermon went on and on this morning and I found myself becoming increasingly bored. There was no cohesive message and the whole thing lacked clarity. I suppose I really ought to spend more time preparing.

HAVING MISHEARD THE NOTICES THAT MORNING STUART
BRINGS CONFUSION TO THE AFTER-SERVICE STEWARDS MEETING

SUNDAY 12 AUGUST

Pippa was complaining today over the supposedly 'barbaric' means we use to keep the children under control during the summer months. I explained to her that with so many ministry leaders away, there has to be an effective means of ensuring the children do not simply run riot throughout the service. She could appreciate it was a demanding time with limited resources, but insisted I make some changes. We eventually came to a compromise and I agreed to loosen their ropes and poke some air holes in the boxes.

NOT A PROMISING START

SUNDAY 19 AUGUST

The trouble with being a pastor is that you're supposed to know the answer to everything. People come up to me in church asking all sorts of questions right out of the blue that I've never even considered before, and they expect some kind of profound answer on the spot! It happened to me today when a student asked me what was the point of home groups — it was terribly awkward.

SUNDAY 26 AUGUST

Cliff got up during testimony time this morning and shared how during the worship he'd experienced a precious touch from the father heart of God, and a powerful tenderness encircled his whole being, filling him with peace and moving him to tears. I don't think I've ever been more embarrassed in my whole life.

CASTING OUT THE SPIRIT OF SANTA

SUNDAY 2 SEPTEMBER

Roger left this morning. Fingers crossed, maybe he'll stay away this time.

MINISTRY TEAM TRAINING

SUNDAY 9 SEPTEMBER

I put out some new collection boxes at the back this morning. After having emptied the box labelled 'For the sick' I've decided to change the sign to 'Financial donations for sick people'.

DONNY WASN'T THE MOST RELIABLE MEMBER OF THE WORSHIP TEAM

THURSDAY 13 SEPTEMBER

The speaker for our 'Breaking the Poverty Mindset' conference has had to cancel. He can't afford the travel unfortunately. We've already paid for the hall and there's no way we're forking out for him too, so I guess we'll just have to find another topic. That shouldn't be too challenging — it's not as if conferences need to be relevant after all.

TONY HAD SOME RESERVATIONS CONCERNING THE NEW GUY

SUNDAY 16 SEPTEMBER

For what must be the fourth week running, all these non-Christians who are attending Mary's Alpha course were coming up to me after the service asking all sorts of questions about Jesus: Is it true he died for them? Can they really have a relationship with him? Does he truly love them? That Alpha course clearly isn't teaching them anything. I'd better shut it down.

THE YOUTH SERVICE:

PROVIDES THE YOUNG
PEOPLE AN OPPORTUNITY
TO EXPRESS THEIR GROWING
CONFIDENCE IN GOD
AND THEIR DEEPENING
UNDERSTANDING
OF THE FAITH

SATURDAY 22 SEPTEMBER

Went to look up a verse in Psalms today but I couldn't find my Bible. I haven't seen it for a while actually. I remember Bunty helping me find the nativity story for last year's Christmas service, but after that it's all a bit of a blank. I would've borrowed one of Cliff's, but I can't read Greek. Oh well, it was only a verse for speaking to the kids tomorrow — I'll just make one up again.

MONDAY 24 SEPTEMBER

Roger has gotten wind of our conference availability, seeing it as a God-given opportunity to shake the church from its current complacency. He has reportedly monitored an alarming rise in the sporting of satanically influenced sideburns and designer beards. Ho hum.

JUST ABOUT THE WORST THING THAT CAN HAPPEN TO YOU IN CHURCH

WEDNESDAY 26 SEPTEMBER

We have ourselves a speaker for the conference! Bestselling author 'Pastor Hank Heals 'Em' is in the country, and can just squeeze the weekend in before flying back to the States. While I am very relieved, I must say that his unusual financial requests worry me somewhat. Any money generated by ticket sales, books, tapes, etc, is to be paid directly to him, in private and in US dollars. He will distribute the cash among his team at a later date as the Lord directs him. I don't see how we can realistically agree to this. Since the conference finishes on a Sunday, there simply won't be time to change the proceeds to dollars before he leaves. It's a bit much to ask really.

FRIDAY 28 SEPTEMBER

I spoke to Pastor Hank tonight. He's agreed to accept pounds sterling. What an accommodating man he is.

BY THE TIME THE DANCING STARTED MIKE WAS DEEPLY REGRETTING NOT TAKING LENNY TO A MORE 'SEEKER FRIENDLY' MEETING

SATURDAY 6 OCTOBER

Had a wonderful time at today's Praise March. Our church fronted the procession and I carried Bunty's JESUS IS ALIVE! banner. It was quite excellent to walk through the city centre proclaiming God's word and holding high the truth for all to see.

SUNDAY 7 OCTOBER

My picture was on the front page of our local paper this morning under the headline: CHURCH'S STARTLING CONFESSION. It would appear I hadn't been holding high the truth as I'd thought, since the 'v' on my banner had unfortunately fallen off at some point. There then followed a rather damning article on the internal confusion of today's church, and its lack of respect in contemporary culture. On the plus side it was a good picture of me.

FRIDAY 12 OCTOBER

Pam has developed some new children's teaching material using cartoon characters to represent spiritual truths. Reading through the strips with her I did wonder if the material was entirely appropriate for the 7–11s. I found it hard, for example, to distinguish between Gerty Grace and Mick Mercy — and the scenes where Andy Anointing keeps falling on Chrissy Christian were perhaps open to misinterpretation. On the plus side, I don't think I've ever seen such a creative rendering of principalities and strongholds.

RUBBISH COUNSELING TECHNIQUES

SUNDAY 21 OCTOBER

Roger came bounding up to me the moment I arrived today. He'd heard that Susan was preaching this morning, and was horrified that I could allow any visible prominence in the church to somebody modelling a selection of casual interchangeable clothing with matching multipurpose accessories, which clearly belonged to the foulest and most vile of creations, spawned in the deepest, darkest recesses of the bowels of hell. I must admit I was speechless — there was no denying he really did have a point this time.

IT BEGAN AS A ROUTINE DELIVERANCE BUT LIONEL SOON FOUND THAT MARY'S DEMON WAS ACTUALLY QUITE CHARMING

Sunday 28 October

Singen brought along his newest invention this morning — a 'Theometer'. It looks like a stubby felt pen but apparently uses a detailed combination of audio, temperature and pressure readings to measure the presence of God. He collected it after the service and took it home to map the Lord's activity over the course of the meeting.

Monday 29 October

Singen phoned up terribly excited! The Theometer revealed an almighty move of the Spirit right after worship, with a steady increase in activity throughout my sermon! Very encouraging.

Tuesday 30 October

Janet chanced to ask me if I'd seen a little felt pen-shaped thing since Sunday. It sounded like the Theometer so I asked where she'd seen it. Apparently she was sitting on it all through my talk.

SATURDAY 3 NOVEMBER

What a great conference this has turned out to be! Pastor Hank is truly inspiring yet so down to earth. There were signs and wonders everywhere tonight. I sat next to a lady whose leg grew a good four inches, although that was actually rather unfortunate in her case, since she only came with a swollen wrist. Thankfully Hank was able to fit her out with one of those orthopaedic shoes left over from the last conference. He's such an accommodating man. Nothing fazes him.

MONDAY 5 NOVEMBER

I can't find my wallet. I remember it being inside my jacket pocket at the airport yesterday, before I hugged Pastor Hank goodbye. But after that it just seemed to disappear. I guess I must have dropped it or something. I did ask God to reveal its whereabouts to me, but all I can think about is Pastor Hank. Such a great guy. A real man of integrity.

INNOVATIVE TECHNIQUES ENCOURAGING PARENTS TO HELP WITH THE CHILDREN'S WORK

SUNDAY 11 NOVEMBER

Cliff wrote a prophecy in my birthday card, confirming my calling and promising incredible future blessing. I think I'm onto him! This is all an elaborate smokescreen to draw my attention away from the suppressed teenage rebellion bubbling away just under the surface. If I can help him to admit it, we can finally throw all this pretence to the wind. He'll cast aside the Christian principles we have taught him, claiming they were forced upon him, and resent any concern for his spiritual welfare. I'll do my best to show I accept him exactly as he is, and gently love him back into the Father's arms. We'll be a normal Christian family at long last!

MONDAY 12 NOVEMBER

I bought Cliff a packet of fags and a six-pack today. I thought if I left them in his room, he'd realize I've seen his true colours and come clean. Unfortunately, Janet found them in my bag. She's insisting I take some time out since the pressure is clearly getting to me. Cliff slipped a note under my door saying that while he was sorry I'd felt it necessary to conceal my addictions from the family, he would still continue to uphold me in prayer and fasting. I wonder if I could hire somebody to follow him to his so-called 'prayer triplet' on Thursday?

ROB AND FRIENDS BLUNDER NOISILY INTO
THE LATECOMERS WORST CASE SCENARIO:
THE PRAYER MEETING THAT'S ALREADY STARTED

SUNDAY 18 NOVEMBER

Roger left again this morning. I wasn't even aware he'd come back.

Sunday 25 November

Sandy rushed up to me this morning terribly concerned over my little Bunty's mental state! There had been a questionnaire in Sunday school and in answering 'Who is Satan?' Bunty had apparently written 'my best friend'! I had to laugh. I reassured Sandy there was no reason to be alarmed — she was not talking about the devil. Satan is just the name Bunty gave to her guinea pig! So there's no need to worry about her!

FRIDAY 30 NOVEMBER

Janet has persuaded me to take some time off with her in the New Year. I am a bit concerned over how the church will fare without me though. I asked her what she thought we should do. She said there must be somebody on the leadership team competent enough to maintain authority and direction while we're gone. I do love Janet. She's such a laugh! Always joking around.

SUNDAY 2 DECEMBER

The rehearsals for the nativity play are shaping up. There were a few set backs using Sandy's two-month-old baby son as Jesus though. I did warn her. While it adds a touch of authenticity to the proceedings, there is undoubtedly more puke than the script calls for.

SUNDAY 9 DECEMBER

Great. We're going away soon and now the car needs major repair work. Our insurance policy doesn't cover 'raving lunatic damage', surprisingly enough. (I thought he'd left anyway.) We are in serious need of a financial miracle!

MONDAY 10 DECEMBER

A financial miracle! It seems a staggering amount of money was left anonymously in yesterday's collection for a 'T. Bold'! Thank you God!

TUESDAY 11 DECEMBER

Typical — the trustees think the money should go to one 'Timothy Bold'. I can't believe it! His whole family are about as uninvolved in church activity as you can get! I pointed out what a ludicrous decision this was to the trustees, but they maintain that since it is not clear who the intended recipient is, they have had to look at who would benefit the most. As a current non-earner, Timothy is in an obviously financially inferior position to myself and the gift goes to him. Quite ridiculous. What on earth a three-year-old is going to do with that kind of money is beyond me.

SUNDAY 16 DECEMBER

Jane asked me to speak to the ministry team today. Some of them have grown discouraged over the perceived lack of spiritual activity during recent ministry times. I reassured them that this was an understandable reaction, and went on to say how important it is that we realize the Holy Spirit is at work the world over, changing entire nations as well as individuals. Consequently, he is of course extremely busy, and any lack of activity is nothing personal. He just has to prioritize. It's not as if he can be everywhere at once after all! Jane said she was glad I was going away, and had I considered making it longer? It's good to know people are behind me.

THE CONGREGATION `WEIGH' ALAN'S WORD

SATURDAY 22 DECEMBER

Had a bit of a falling out with Sandy over my 'job' in the nativity play. I'd been responsible for making the wise men's gold, frankincense and myrrh — which I'd completed thoughtfully and creatively in my opinion. But it wasn't good enough for Sandy, who claimed they weren't authentic enough. She said the wise men simply wouldn't have used wrapping paper. Yeah right. They were gifts — it was Christmas! Everybody wraps Christmas presents! Some people don't know a thing.

GEOFF ARRIVES AT THE BOXING DAY SERVICE WITHOUT A CHRISTMAS JUMPER ON

WEDNESDAY 2 JANUARY

I've asked Vincent to lead the church while we're away. He was pretty surprised, but extremely flattered to realize I was so aware of his gifting and aspirations. I didn't tell him that when I'd picked his name out of the hat I'd had to ask Janet who he was.

THE ALTERNATIVE SERVICE: A CONTEMPORARY APPROACH TO EXPLORING BIBLICAL TRUTHS THROUGH CREATIVE AND MEANINGFUL EXPERIMENTATION

SATURDAY 12 JANUARY

Got up early and drove to the bus station. We'd packed all our stuff onto the coach and I was sitting there gazing out of the window when I noticed Roger. He was talking to somebody across the street and pointing frantically at their shoes. My heart sank as I realized it was Vincent. The bus started. I began praying earnestly that Vincent would turn round and run for dear life, or laugh in Roger's face, or kill him there and then. Instead he took off his shoes and threw them away. The bus pulled off and I began to cry.

THE PRAYER MEETING LOSES ITS FOCUS